BEST OF BIFF

CHRIS GARRATT and MICK KIDD

i
impact books

This edition first published in Great Britain 1992
by Impact Books, 112 Bolingbroke Grove,
London SW11 1DA.

ISBN 1 874687 02 1

Printed and bound in Guernsey by
The Guernsey Press Company Ltd.

ADVENTURES IN CONVERSATION
4. DEALING WITH THE MALE EGO
I'D LIKE TO GO ON ABOUT MYSELF AT GREAT LENGTH IF THAT'S OKAY.
THAT'D BE FINE, KEN, HONESTLY... BUT I'M LATE FOR A REHEARSAL ALREADY. INCIDENTALLY, DID YOU KNOW YOU'VE GOT YOUR ELBOW IN YOUR LASAGNE?

'**I Predict the Future**'

—WEATHERMAN'S AMAZING CLAIM

THEME FOR A DREAM

TRAVELLIN' LIGHT

Round 7: At Home with the Stars

QUESTION TIME! ★ ★ ★ ★

1. From the textual clues available account for the demise of the screen goddess.
2. Using subtitles where appropriate continue this domestic tearjerker in the style of (a) Ingmar Bergman, (b) Antonioni, (c) Hammer Horror

The Women's Committee also felt that more women should be on the main committee to represent certain areas of women's experience. So the following were elected:

3 black/ethnic minority women; 1 lesbian; 1 trade unionist; 1 woman with disabilities; 1 older woman.

The Joys of Communal Living.

"O" LEVEL COUNTER CULTURE

Timewarp allowed: 3 hours. Do not scrawl situationist graffiti in the margins or stub your rollups in the inkwells. Orange may be worn. Credit will be given to candidates who self actualise.

1. Compare and contrast Pink Floyd with Black Sabbath and say why neither has street credibility.

2. "Even Buddha would have been hard pushed to reach Nirvana squatting on a juggernaut route." Consider the dialectic of inner truth and inner city.

3. Write notes on three of the following:
   a) Leylines. b) 1969 Moon Landing. c) Jung d) Woodstock. e) Tai Chi. f) Red Leb.

4. "The Egomaniac's Liberation Front were a bunch of revisionist ripoff merchants." Comment on this insult.

5. Account for the lack of references to brown rice in Dylan's lyrics.

6. Which is the most hassle: a) being paranoid a black hole is about to suck you into it, b) NME dismissing your concept album as idoelogically unsound heavy metal dross.

7. Write an essay either on rebirthing or why you think Leonard Cohen's great.

8. "Casteneda was a bit of a bozo." How far is this a fair summing up of western dualism?

9. A racket or a rocket to the unconscious? Provide a radical critique of meditation.

10. Hermann Hesse was a pisces. Discuss.

EXAMINATION FEE: £250

How To Behave At A Preview

'O' LEVEL LOVE

Answer **ONE** question.

1. Account for Barry's zero credibility with women, making reference to EITHER (a) his oral fixation' OR (b) his atrocious taste in sports jackets.
2. Assuming Tessa's role, describe 3 possible alternatives to snogging, (e.g.: going to the pictures, revolutionary socialism).

Make money !
BE A HACK WRITER

££££££££££££££££££

Expert advice from a well known con merchant; LEARN how to write like Borges in hours. Discover the simplicity of Mallarme, Goethe and Proust. Dostoevsky made easy, Shakespearean style *yours* for as little as £200 for seven week correspondence course inclusive of plagiarism, court costs etc.

COMMUNICATIONS AND THE CURRICULUM
An Introduction to Media Studies

PRISONER of GENDER

HE WAS YOUNG AND UPWARDLY MOBILE..

FADS OF THE 80s
22: EATING OUT

The CreaTive Process

2: ANXIETY

A ROOM OF MY OWN

He opens the door to his scruffy little flat in the seedier end of London's Portobello Road and greets you with an apology about the state of the place.

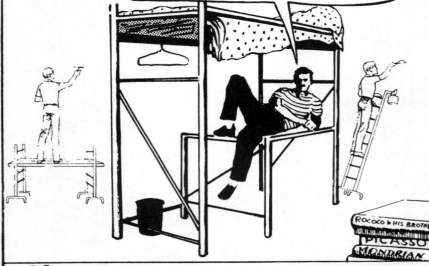

I HOPE TO FEATURE PERMANENT INDOOR SCAFFOLDING, CHUNKY DOORKNOBS, ART DECO LAMPS, '50's TAT, HIGH-TECH SPOTLIGHTS, GARDEN FURNITURE, ANYTHING ETHNIC, BAUHAUS BOOKCASES AND POP-OUT GITANE ASHTRAYS IF MY ENTERPRISE ALLOWANCE COMES THROUGH.

NEXT: ATMOSPHERE IN A TEENAGER'S DEN, PLUS HOW TO LIVEN UP A LANDING.

ESCAPE TO FULFILMENT

**A THERAPY GROWTH GROUP
IN A HOLIDAY SETTING**

First class therapy, exciting food and
interesting people.
Families welcome.

YOUNG GUNS GO FOR IT

1. SHOULD QUANTUM PHYSICS BE KEPT OUT OF SPORT?
2. COMPARE AND CONTRAST TRANMERE ROVERS WITH STENHOUSMUIR.

SUDDENLY LAST SUMMER

FAMOUS BOZOS No. 9
MORE SEATING UPSTAIRS
IT'S NOT YOU... —IT'S JUST THAT I'M A GENIUS - I HAVE TO HAVE MY SPACE!
SNORE
ZZZZZZZZZ

GREAT HIPPY CLICHES Nº 5
NEVER TRUST ANYONE OVER 30 35 40 45
Fried Egg Sandwiches 35p
Rainbow Trips
STEAL THIS BOOK ABBIE HOFFMAN
Candles 30p

MEN ABOUT TOWN

WALKING BACK TO HAPPINESS
DO YOU REMEMBER THE WINDSOR FREE FESTIVAL OF '74?
COME ON, BEN, — TIME FOR YOUR VAN MORRISON.
NICE ONE.
FUTURE EVENTS
BALINESE TEMPLE DANCING
plus
"I WAS THERE" talk on Paris 68 Riots by Eric
CHINESE WHITE
SUNSHINE SUPERMAN
COHEN

BLAME IT ON THE
BOSSANOVA
LAST ORDERS 11·30 PM.
MATTER IS SIMPLY A CONVENIENT NAME FOR WHAT'S HAPPENING WHERE IT ISN'T, ANDRE.
SOCRATIC DIALOGUE
DON'T LOOK AT ME, I'M JUST A MENTAL EVENT.
COULD WE HAVE THE DAMAGE?
SEEMING CANDLE.
DRAMA TEACHER
B.R.
OUT TO LUNCH

Fads of the Me Decade:
CONSCIOUSNESS RAISING
HI- IS THIS THE GROUP DYNAMICS CLASS?
I AM EXPERIENCING THE OTHERS EXPERIENCING ME EXPERIENCING THEM?
WHO IS THIS I ASKING WHO IS THIS I?
I EXIST BUT EVERYONE ELSE MAY BE A FIGMENT OF MY IMAGINATION
I AM A WORTHWHILE PERSON